Digging up Memories

from you to me®

from you to me®

concept by Neil Coxon

Digging up Memories

from you to me®

This gardening journal is for the anecdotes and tips from your family or friends.

It will capture their experiences and secrets from their time with plants, gardens, the countryside or indeed anywhere that things grow.

Ask them to complete it carefully and, if they want to, add some photographs, clippings or even some pressed flowers.

When it is finished and returned to you, this will be a record of an amazing collection of advice and stories that you will treasure forever.

Dear

Here is a gift from me to you . . . for you to give to me.

Gardening can be a hobby or a way of life for people and I can clearly remember some of the wonderful things you have grown over the years and the stories you have told me.

Please can you capture some of your experiences for me along with your answers to my questions about your life in, and with, gardens. There may be some questions that you can't or don't want to answer, so don't worry, just complete the ones you like.

People say that we all have at least one book in us, and this will be one of yours.

The story of you, your gardens and gardening that I will treasure forever.

Thank you,

with love

"No two gardens are the same.
No two days are the same in one garden"

Hugh Johnson

Your own story of you and the garden ...

What are your **earliest memories** of your time in the garden?

What plants evoke memories of your childhood?

Where does your interest in gardens and gardening stem from?

What were the first plants you remember growing?

How did you **learn** about gardening?

Tell me about the **most successful** plants you have grown . . .

Tell me some of your **funniest** gardening
memories . . .

What would be in your 'top 10' list of favourite plants and why?

Tell me about some of the other favourites
in your garden . . .

Flower . . .

Tree . . .

Place . . .

Time of day . . .

Smell . . .

Texture . . .

Colour . . .

Visitors . . .

Tell me about some favourite gardens you have seen or visited …

Who has most **influenced** your interest in gardens and gardening?

And **who** would be your favourite **gardener**?

What are some of the most unusual plants you have ever grown?

What books, programmes or websites on gardening would you recommend?

What traditions do you follow when it comes to gardening?

Which season do you prefer and why?

Tell me about your most memorable day in a garden . . .

Animals are often attracted to gardens.
Tell me some stories about your encounters . . .

What are the greatest changes you have noticed in gardening throughout your life?

How have you noticed **changes** in the **climate** affecting your plants or gardening?

Describe your favourite gardening design

. . . and perhaps sketch it for me opposite.

Villages often run gardening competitions.
Tell me some stories about any you have experienced . . .

Tell me about some of the gardening tools or gadgets you have used or invented . . .

What would be your favourite meal made with fresh produce from your garden?

Please give me a recipe you have used to make a drink or meal from the things you have grown or found growing . . .

What are some of your most memorable quotes or rhymes about gardening?

If you could **invite anyone** from the past or present to your garden, who would they be and why?

Describe what would be your 'perfect day' in the garden . . .

With regard to gardening, what would you still like us to do together?

If you were to have a plant named after you or planted in your memory, what would it be and why?

What other **anecdotes** and **stories** can you tell me about your time in the garden?

Your own advice and expertise ...

What ideas do you have to encourage children to take an interest in gardening or growing plants?

What techniques would you recommend when it comes to planting seeds or taking cuttings?

Weather has a big influence on our gardening successes. What suggestions do you have on how to make the most of it . . .

Which of the animals you have had in your garden/s were friends and which were foes?

There are many **tales** about techniques to **protect** or **remove** pests or diseases from your plants . . . which ones have you followed?

On the vegetable patch ... what would you suggest I grow?

Can you recommend any **varieties** of vegetables that you believe do best?

What advice would you give me about growing fruit?

"A garden without flowers is like a day without sunshine"

What flowers do you like and which have you successfully grown?

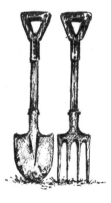

If I wanted to have a **perfect lawn** like a bowling green in my garden . . . what would you suggest?

What top-tips could you give me about having a **water feature** in my garden?

What successes have you had with indoor plants?

Not everyone has a large garden so what tips could you give about growing flowers or vegetables in containers or baskets?

Plants that heal ... which plants do you think have beneficial properties?

How have you dealt with **weeds**?

Which ones have you **removed** and which have

you **encouraged**?

Organic gardening is becoming more prevalent . . . what views and advice would you give me?

Gardening can be expensive . . . what top-tips do you have on **saving money?**

Soil can be very different in varying locations . . . what do I need to know to get the best from it?

How do you manage a compost heap ...

What do you put in it and what do you keep out?

Companion planting is where some plants benefit from **growing near** each other . . . what have you observed?

How should I organise my plants and time in a greenhouse?

A lot of success in the garden comes from doing the right things at the right time.

Please draw up your list of the main things I should be doing at particular times of the year...

Many edible things grow wild in fields or hedgerows. Please tell me what I should look out for and how to use it . . .

It is said you don't own a wood, you just tend it for the next generation.

Tell me about the trees you have grown, tended or simply been near during your gardening life . . .

Some more Old Wives' Tales ...

Oak before Ash, we're in for a splash
Ash before Oak, we're in for a soak

St Swithin's Day if thou does rain,
for forty days it will remain . . .

Which tales have you heard or followed?

These extra pages are for us to write any gardening
questions, memories or answers that
may not have been covered elsewhere in the journal . . .

And finally for the record . . .

what is your full name ?

what is your date of birth ?

what was the date when you completed this journal for me ?

tell me where the gardens you have tended have been . . .

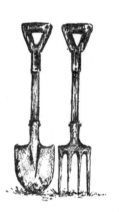

Dear

I will treasure this book, your tips and your memories forever.

I hope you enjoyed completing it and answering my questions.

Thank you so much for doing it and for writing your own book about you and your love of gardening . . .

from you to me

Digging up Memories
from you to me®

First published in the UK by *from you to me*, April 2010
Copyright, *from you to me* limited 2010
Hackless House, Murhill, Bath, BA2 7FH
www.fromyoutome.com
E-mail: hello@fromyoutome.com

ISBN 978-1-907048-15-9

Cover design by so design consultants, Wick, Bristol, UK
Pen & Ink illustrations by Barbara Jaques
Printed and bound in the UK by CPI William Clowes, Beccles

This paper is manufactured from material sourced from forests certified according to strict environmental, social and economical standards.

If you think other questions should be included in future editions, please let us know. And please share some of the interesting answers you receive with us at the *from you to me* website to let other people read about these fascinating insights . . .

If you liked the concept of this book, please tell your family and friends and look out for others in the *from you to me* range:

Dear Mum, from you to me
Dear Dad, from you to me
Dear Grandma, from you to me
Dear Grandad, from you to me
Dear Sister, from you to me
Dear Brother, from you to me
Dear Daughter, from you to me
Dear Son, from you to me

Dear Friend, from you to me
Cooking up Memories, from you to me
These were the days, from you to me
Christmas Present, Christmas Past, from you to me

other relationship and memory journals available soon . . .